Date Due

A War Job

"Thought Impossible"

Phantom-view of a gyro-compass and its accessory equipment.

A War Job
"Thought Impossible"

by

Wesley W. Stout

Chrysler Corporation

Detroit, Michigan

1945

The delivery of the 5,500th Sperry gyro-compass made by Chrysler Corporation, Rear Admiral E. L. Cochrane, Chief of the Bureau of Ships, United States Navy, wrote, "will mark the completion of one of industry's war contracts originally considered impossible..."

Foreword

OUR business is principally the making of passenger cars and trucks. In the crisis of war, we took on, among many weapons and munitions, the making of this complex precision instrument, the Sperry gyro-compass. We did so in the belief that the principles of engineered production, developed during years of peace-time manufacturing, could be applied to the making of this intricate device so unlike anything in our past experience. The story told in the following pages speaks for itself.

The compass, in design and engineering, is wholly the creation of the Sperry Gyroscope Company, to whom all credit for the magic of its performance belongs. Without the enthusiastic support of the Navy personnel assigned to this contract, and the cooperation of Sperry, Chrysler Corporation could not quickly have accomplished the first quantity production of this sensitive and vitally important mechanism.

K. T. KELLER
President

The Dodge plant in which Chrysler made this exquisitely exact mechanism for the Navy.

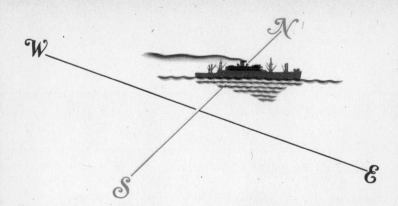

The other day* Chrysler completed one of its war jobs.

This was the making of 5,500 gyro-compasses for the Navy.

The contract was a minor one dollarwise compared with tanks or super bomber engines, though as much as the Corporation earned in such recent years as 1938 and 1939. The product will never kill an enemy, yet it is as vital to the war as a Bofors anti-aircraft gun or a tank.

A gyro-compass is an extremely sensitive and exact mechanism, though not a little one; this model, with accessories, weighed upwards of 1,300 pounds. In the past they were made a few at a time and partly by hand by workmen of high specialized skills.

The Chrysler Corporation made them by engineered production methods—that is, speedily and in large numbers, using workers of no or ordinary skills who never had seen a gyro-compass until then.

*February, 1945

R. G. Knight, Superintendent, Gyro-Compass Department.

Fred J. Lamborn, Vice-President and General Manager of the Dodge Division.

No compass ever was returned to the Corporation as defective.

In order to manufacture a precision instrument with ordinary labor, management broke the compass and its machining down into simple components and operations easily taught a novice, so engineered the tooling that the accuracy was transferred from the mechanic to the machine tool.

Chrysler built these compasses for 55% of the originally estimated cost. It took the contract at a

A. B. Kirsch,
Master Mechanic.

A. C. Sachse, Elec-
trical Engineer.

George W. Malcomson,
Liaison Representative.

figure set by the Navy, which had been buying compasses for many years but now needed many more
than existing facilities and trained working force
could produce.

The over-all cost of 5,500 compasses, including
spares and ordered extra equipment, under the esti-
mate fixed in the first contract would have been
$42,689,000. The actual cost to the Government was
approximately $23,479,000—a saving of $19,210,000
to the taxpayers.

Before: Floor space vacated for the gyro-compass job.

After: A corner of the gyro machine shop six months later.

When the 5,500th compass came off the assembly line February 9, 1945, the flagship signalled "Well Done," the Navy accolade.

"The completion of this compass," Rear Admiral E. L. Cochrane, chief of the Bureau of Ships, wrote the Corporation, "will mark the completion of one of industry's war contracts originally considered impossible; that is, the manufacture of an intricate, delicate gyro-compass by other than a manufacturer especially trained and skilled in the art.

"A recital of all the important and interesting facts of this achievement would take volumes. It is, however, of particular interest to note that it was on February 5, 1942, that two representatives of the Bureau first approached Dodge with a request that they consider the manufacture of gyro-compasses. Including that day, and until this ninth day of February, 1945, which marks the completion of the five

Ships still must steer by compass, despite other aids to navigation, old and new. Until recent years, the compass was a magnetized needle. Few of man's tools had changed so little in centuries. It was the same needle with the same failings which Columbus had followed to a new world, and even less dependable in modern steel ships than it was in his wooden caravels. Yet until the late Dr. Elmer A. Sperry invented the gyroscopic compass about 1910, there was no other kind.

When accurate, the magnetized needle does not index true North, and it seldom is accurate. It is deflected by the metals of the ship, by the knife in the pocket of the helmsman, by magnetic disturbances in the air such as cause the static in your radio, and by ore deposits in nearby land. There are waters and times when it is worse than useless.

If you ever have spun a top and rolled a hoop, you can understand how a gyroscope works. The top stands upright while it spins, contrary to the law of gravity, its spinning force being greater than gravitational pull. If a boy picks up a spinning top in the palm of his hand and tilts his palm back and forth, the top goes on spinning erectly, ignoring this shifting of its base. This escape from the dictatorship of gravity is called gyroscopic inertia and is true of all

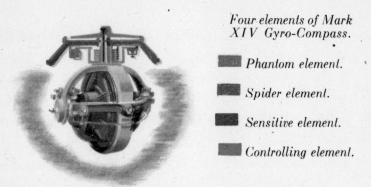

Four elements of Mark
XIV Gyro-Compass.

Phantom element.

Spider element.

Sensitive element.

Controlling element.

spinning things, though not visible in all. The earth itself is a mammoth gyroscope. If it did not revolve like a top with its polar axis fairly constant, life could not exist here, due to the rapid and extreme changes from heat to cold.

Man long has known about gyroscopic inertia, but had not put it to practical use. A gyro-compass harnesses this freak of nature. The heart of such a compass is a heavy, solid bronze wheel called a rotor which, enclosed in a squirrel-cage motor, spins much faster than any top. Suspended from above, the rotor is free to turn on all three of its axes. Put another way, only one point—the geometrical center of its supporting system—is a fixed position, the wheel being free to turn in any direction around this point.

This means that when a ship rolls and pitches, the

9

*Five thousand tools, jigs, dies and fixtures were
specially designed and installed for this job.*

More than a quarter of the compass workers were women; very few with any previous factory experience.

gyro holds its own plane of rotation, unchanged by any motion of the ship. Build a gyroscope large enough and it will prevent the ship itself from rolling with the waves. But this is not all: the rotor ignores the earth's rotation just as it does the ship's tossing. Its plane of rotation does not shift as the earth turns. In this sense, it is a little sun, cockily operating in its own solar system.

So far, this is no help toward finding the North. An ordinary compass needle is pulled toward North by the attraction of the magnetic pole. North is an earthly direction and the gyro has declared its in-

11

dependence of the earth. There are no directions in space where it spins, so of itself it can indicate no direction. As it refuses to follow the earth's axis of rotation, its own rotational axis must be changing constantly in relation to any given point on this earth, such as the North pole.

Repeater compass assembly; Dodge made and shipped five repeaters with each master compass.

Any gyroscope is, in a sense, a little sun operating in its own solar system and oblivious of the earth.

Here Dr. Sperry introduced a second physical phenomenon, another freak of nature which scientists call precession. When a boy wants to turn his rolling hoop, he taps it with a stick, but not at the front or back as it would be natural to suppose. Though he does not know why, he puts the pressure on the top of the hoop as if he intended to tip the hoop over. Due to its rolling gyroscopic energy, it resists the stick's pressure and turns away at right angles. By this law, any force applied to either the horizontal or vertical axis of the gyro rotor is felt 90 degrees away. Apply pressure to the horizontal axis and the gyroscope turns or precesses on its vertical axis; apply the force to the vertical axis and it turns on its horizontal axis.

A frame supporting four cups of mercury and called a "ballistic" does for the rotor what the boy's stick does to the hoop. Mercury is a very heavy, liquid

metal and so is very sensitive to gravity. As the earth turns from West to East, one side of the ballistic tends to rise, the other to drop. The mercury feeds through connecting tubes from the high to the low side to restore the level. In doing this, Dr. Sperry made it exert this precessive force.

The rest is automatic. As the earth always revolves from West to East and as precession always is felt 90 degrees away from the point of application, then the gyro spinning axis is forced to right angles from West-East. This right angle is South-North. While the earth goes on turning and the mercury column goes on compensating, the mercury constantly kicks the rotor back on the South-North meridian. A compass card or azimuth ring with its zero graduation aligned with the rotating axis of the gyro then always will register true north.

Girl drill press operator on the bronze repeater case. It must be vacuum-exhausted, impregnated with varnish and baked to close its pores.

Being deflected by no forces in or exterior to the ship, a gyro-compass may be located anywhere, though preferably below decks at the vessel's center of gravity, with repeater compasses on the bridge, in the captain's cabin, at bow and stern and wherever else desired. A magnetic compass, so sensitive to magnetic metals, must be isolated on the bridge in the most exposed position to battle damage. In fact, it is now the practice of our Navy to install the magnetic compass in the crow's nest, high up in the foremast, with a repeater dial on the bridge. Navy ships still carry magnetic compasses in case of battle damage to the gyro-compass.

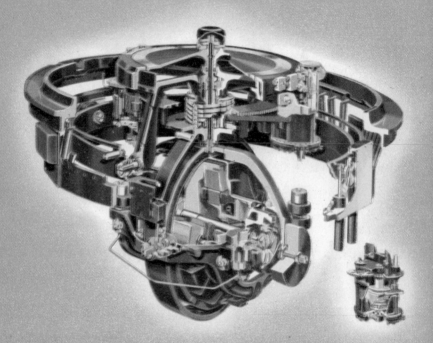

Cut-away drawing of the "sensitive mechanism," as the heart of the gyro-compass is known to the trade.

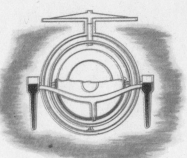

Mercury ballistic containers.

A gyro-compass cost so much, however, that only passenger liners and larger warships commonly were so equipped until the Nazis loosed their magnetic mines in 1941. These were pulled into passing ships by the magnetic attraction of the ship's steel plates and machinery.

The British found a quick answer. This De Gaussing belt, which reversed a ship's magnetic field, defeated the magnetic mine, but it also destroyed the already wobbly accuracy of magnetic compasses. Every deep water ship now needed a gyro-compass. This sudden demand coincided with our enormous shipbuilding program. Hence a quick necessity for gyro-compasses in numbers undreamed of until now, for old ships and new.

There were only two sources, Sperry and the Arma Engineering Corporation, both neighbors of the Brooklyn Navy Yard. Neither was set up for mass

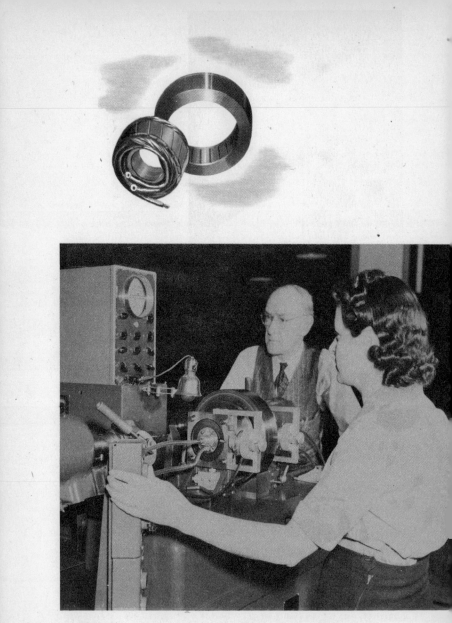

This electronic rotor balancing device is so delicate that it discovers variations of as little as 1/10,000th of an ounce.

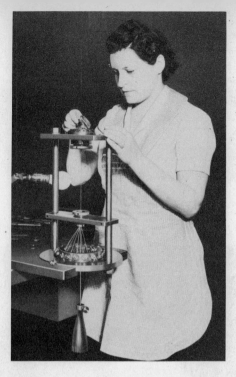

Examined under a microscope, the eighteen tiny suspension wires must form a perfect circle with a hair-sized opening down the center.

production. The Navy first planned to expand these plants, but after Pearl Harbor, a vision of one blockbuster bomb knocking out the Yard, Sperry, Arma and the Brooklyn and Manhattan bridges sent the Navy looking for a new source far removed. After a country-wide survey, it chose Detroit and Chrysler, proposing that the Corporation take over from Sperry the manufacture of the Mark XIV model, an intermediate size.

When Captain Huse and Commander Hall walked into President Keller's office that February day of 1942, Mr. Keller had no knowledge of their errand.

Unit-testing of sub-assemblies is a Chrysler tradition; rotors were run 18 hours at operating speed before final assembly.

When he had heard it, he thought a moment. All plants were loaded up by then with war jobs, Dodge as much as any, but Dodge was a plant into which one more job might be squeezed.

He phoned the office of Fred Lamborn, Vice President of the Dodge division in charge of manufacturing, asking that some key men be sent over to talk about a new job. The two Navy officers had brought along a prospectus containing a description

Inspecting repeater motors, held to the same exacting standards of precision as the master compass.

of the compass, but without drawings. It told a mechanic little of what he would want to know. Mr. Keller handed the book to one of Lamborn's men, A. B. Kirsch. Kirsch is an exquisite mechanic who had worked in the Dodge tool room since 1914, the kind of craftsman not interested in a job unless it challenges his ingenuity.

He glanced at the frontispiece and commented: "Oh, a Sperry gyro-compass." With which he de-

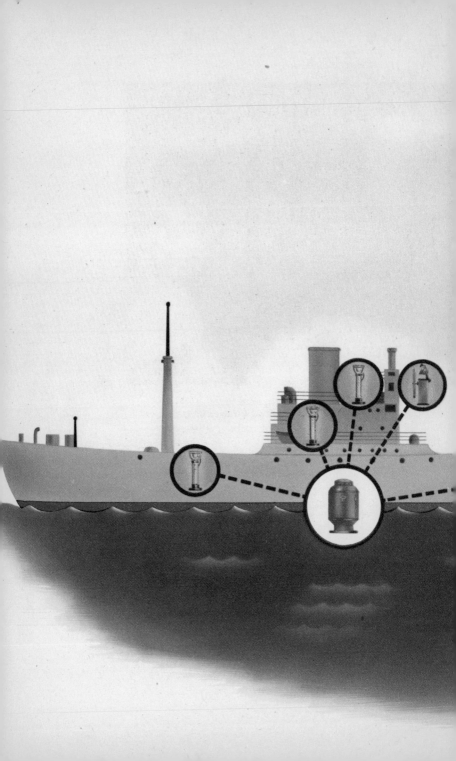

The master compass is installed within the body of the ship, preferably at its center of gravity, with repeater dials on the bridge; in the Master's cabin and wherever else desired.

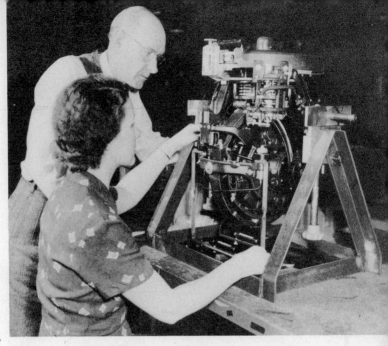

Checking the exact balance of the mercury ballistic before final assembly.

Weighing the mercury which transforms the gyro from an interesting toy into an infallible compass.

scribed the insides of the instrument more usefully than did the book.

"Can we make them?" the President asked the Dodge delegation.

"Why not?," they said. "We ought to get a sample compass, though, and first have a good look at it."

Captain Huse said he would gladly borrow a compass from the Brooklyn Navy Yard. Mr. Keller buzzed for a secretary, told him to get the Navy Yard on the phone for Huse. "Ask them," he told the captain, "to load it on tonight's Detroiter. We want it here in the morning."

"But it weighs more than half a ton!" Huse exclaimed.

"If you want action, having it here in the morning is more important than the cost of getting it here then," was the answer.

The call came through. After Huse had hung up,

Commander Hall had an afterthought, exclaiming: "We should have thought to ask them to send along an expert to disassemble the compass for Dodge."

"Somebody put it together," spoke up Kirsch. "I guess we can take it apart."

This was a Thursday. Before Monday morning, the sample compass was broken down into its individual pieces and sub-assemblies for the study of Dodge

Final assembly of the repeater compasses, of which Dodge built and shipped 26,882.

Sailors call them peloris stands, a hard name for the containers of deck-installed repeater compasses. Dodge built 11,000 of these.

At peak production, twelve master compasses a day passed through these final assembly lines, and Dodge could easily have made more.

master mechanics. By the following Thursday, Mr. Keller led a group of Dodge men to Brooklyn to make sure that the Sperry drawings and specifications were in condition to permit immediate manufacture. In the group were Lamborn, Dick Knight, who was to become superintendent of the gyro shop; Art Sasche, the electrical engineer assigned to the contract; and Kirsch, appointed master mechanic.

Back in Detroit the next morning, eight days after Huse's and Hall's visit, Mr. Keller wired the Cor-

Gently lowering the gyro-compass into its binnacle.

The empty binnacle.

Binnacles are put together on assembly lines.

poration's acceptance of the assignment to make 1,000 Mark XIV compasses.

A letter of intent came from the Navy on March 23rd in advance of a formal contract. The Navy does not tell one contractor what it pays another. Lacking all cost information, the Corporation accepted an estimated price of $7,500 a compass, on the Navy's assurance that this was a fair figure.

This was a cost and fixed fee contract. Cost plus contracts became notorious in World War I. The contractor being paid a percentage of his costs, the greater the cost the greater his profit became. By the cost and fixed fee method of World War II, the Government and the contractor agree in advance on an estimated cost. The contractor is paid a fixed fee. Whether the actual cost is found to be lower or higher, his fee is supposed to be unchanged. His costs are, of course, scrutinized and approved by the Government before he gets his money. His profits are subject to final renegotiation if the Government thinks they are excessive.

The cost and fixed fee contract is suspect in Congress. Its critics say that it does not protect the Government sufficiently; that it encourages a sloppy job by neither rewarding savings nor penalizing waste. A very close approximation of costs on this contract now is available.

The north-finding mechanism itself. If you have spun a top or rolled a hoop, you can understand its magic.

Though the first several hundred compasses cost well more than the estimated $7,500, the Corporation lowered the cost so continuously that the average cost, excluding spare parts, was about $4,098; including spare parts it was about $4,269. This figure would have been lower still but for engineering and equipment changes made from time to time at Navy direction, and had the Navy's needs warranted production at capacity.

No part of these savings went into Chrysler's pocket. Its compensation was governed by the estimated costs. These were lowered on the second contract and successively as the Corporation perfected its manufacturing methods. The Corporation's fee would have been $2,573,105 on the basis of the originally estimated cost. Actually, Chrysler was paid $2,009,242, a saving of $563,863 in the Government's favor. This, added to $19,210,000 reduction from the originally estimated manufacturing cost, makes a total saving of nearly twenty millions of dollars to the taxpayers.

Much of the manufacturing equipment was rented from the Government at a cost to Chrysler of $391,-000. It cost $1,037,000 to tool up for the first 1,000 units at a production rate of four a day. It cost only $163,000 for the added facilities with which to double production to eight daily. When the Navy asked

Dodge for twelve daily, the further facilities cost a mere $60,000, a striking example of the economies of engineered production methods.

The first compass was accepted by the Navy on September 11, 1942, and shipped direct to Benton Harbor, Mich., for installation on a new mine-sweeper. It had first been assembled six weeks earlier, registering the outrageous error of 28.2 degrees, or enough to deflect a ship sailing for Liverpool to the bulge of Africa. Dodge men repeatedly took it apart

The rotor is "cold," i.e., not turning, when lowered into the binnacle.

and put it together again, checking every detail with blueprints and specifications, without reducing the error, let alone correcting it. The Navy's resident inspectors tried their hands with no better luck.

By a process of elimination, the error was traced to the mercury ballistic, yet every dimension here was closer than the Sperry prints dictated or the Navy enforced. When the ballistic was removed, however, and that of the Sperry sample substituted, the No. 1 compass quickly settled out to within 2 degrees of North.

There is a breather in the ballistic to allow the escape of air as the mercury flows back and forth. In the breather is a strand of wool intended to keep dust out. The specifications called merely for a 6-inch strand of white wool yarn. There was no mention of weight or twist.

When the wicking bought by Chrysler under these specifications was compared it was found to be markedly different from the loosely twisted wicking of the Sperry sample compass. The denser wick was interfering with the escape of air and so slowing the compensating flow of the Mercury. The "bug" was in the seemingly least important detail of a precision instrument, a bit of wool. With a strand of ordinary knitting yarn bought in the nearest 5-and-10, the first compass settled out to an error of .1 degrees, or substantial perfection.

As with all war contracts, there was an unceasing battle for machines, tools and materials, and the inevitable agonizing disappointments, but on the day before Christmas of 1942 the gyro shop delivered its 100th unit as a stocking present for the Navy. The 200th compass set out for sea on January 18, 1943. In that month Dodge shipped 160 compasses against a Navy rated capacity of 100 on its machinery.

The Navy now was asking Dodge to move up from four to eight a day and in March Dodge shipped 215

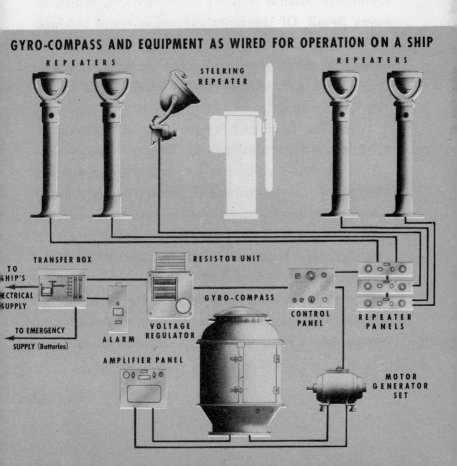

GYRO-COMPASS AND EQUIPMENT AS WIRED FOR OPERATION ON A SHIP

REPEATERS

STEERING REPEATER

REPEATERS

TRANSFER BOX

RESISTOR UNIT

TO SHIP'S ELECTRICAL SUPPLY

GYRO-COMPASS

CONTROL PANEL

REPEATER PANELS

TO EMERGENCY SUPPLY (Batteries)

VOLTAGE REGULATOR

ALARM

AMPLIFIER PANEL

MOTOR GENERATOR SET

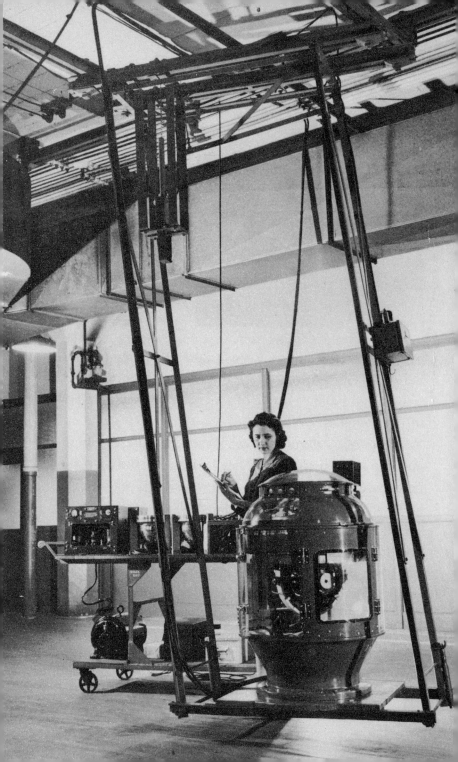

As with all war contracts, there was an unceasing battle for machines, tools and materials, and the inevitable agonizing disappointments, but on the day before Christmas of 1942 the gyro shop delivered its 100th unit as a stocking present for the Navy. The 200th compass set out for sea on January 18, 1943. In that month Dodge shipped 160 compasses against a Navy rated capacity of 100 on its machinery.

The Navy now was asking Dodge to move up from four to eight a day and in March Dodge shipped 215

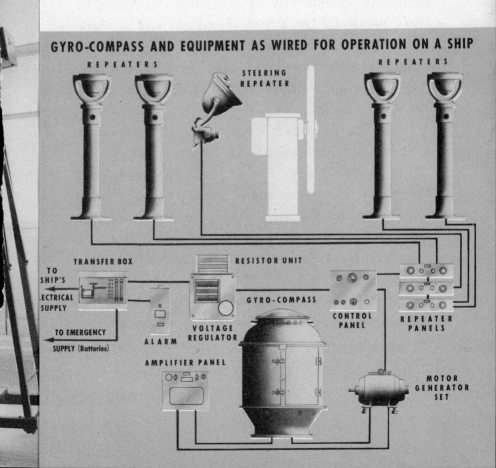

GYRO-COMPASS AND EQUIPMENT AS WIRED FOR OPERATION ON A SHIP

REPEATERS

STEERING REPEATER

REPEATERS

TRANSFER BOX

TO SHIP'S ELECTRICAL SUPPLY

TO EMERGENCY SUPPLY (Batteries)

ALARM

RESISTOR UNIT

VOLTAGE REGULATOR

GYRO-COMPASS

AMPLIFIER PANEL

CONTROL PANEL

REPEATER PANELS

MOTOR GENERATOR SET

units, better than this doubled rate. In the last days of 1943, the Bureau of Ships asked the Corporation to go to twelve a day, authorizing the additional machinery and equipment. This production rate was reached in the first week of April, 1944. It was not continued only because the Navy meanwhile had found that supply had overtaken demand.

The theory of the compass has been described. This theory can be translated into effect only if the mechanism is in exquisitely exact balance, and such balance is possible only by micrometric accuracy in every detail. Of the ten thousand parts of a Mark XIV compass, the cases are the only metal not machined to micro accuracy, some parts to one ten-thousandth of an inch, or about one-fiftieth the thickness of human hair.

When the 50-pound bronze rotor is spinning at 6,000 revolutions a minute, it must be with so little vibration that a dime can be balanced edgewise on the case. Until the rotor is in perfect balance, every disproportion is registered on a screen by the rapidly moving finger of an electronic device called a cathode ray oscillograph. It not only reports the condition, but points out the location.

The rotor is suspended by a strand of eighteen fine wires, each nine one-thousandths in diameter and identical in length and tension. Examined under a

38

Final inspection-before swing test.

pe, they must form a perfect circle with a
d open space down the center. This precise
nd balance is one of the many critical details
mpass.

aster compass being located within the ship
rotor being hermetically-sealed in an alumi-
e, the binnacle or outer casing is merely a
    But the cases of the repeater compasses,
ch also seem to the lay eye to be mere jackets of
functional consequence, are exhausted in a vacu-
; then in order to fill their bronze pores, they are
regnated with an impervious lacquer under 30-
ls pressure and baked at a high temperature
        d a half hours. They must be both water

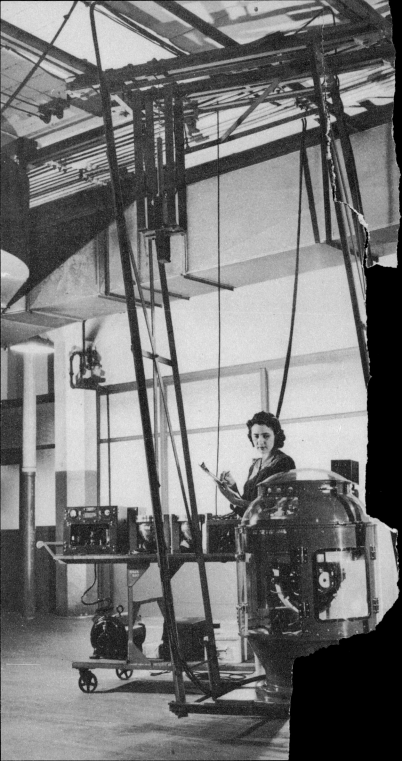

and air-proof. Exposed on deck, the repeaters may be submerged by waves, while air produces moisture under condensation.

A basic reason for Dodge's success with this strange and delicate instrument was the Chrysler tradition of unit testing of sub-assemblies before final assembly. For example, Dodge makes the transmissions for all Chrysler cars in normal times. Each set of gears is tested for noise and run-out before they are assembled into a transmission. When sub-assemblies are checked carefully, errors are caught and corrected before final assembly, with marked savings of time and money.

←For two days and nights, each compass is rocked back and forth in these test room swings like so many summer boarders.

The accessories which go with each gyro-compass move up on special trucks to be calibrated and tied-in electrically with the master compass as the latter goes into its final examinations.

The Scorsby testing machine simulates the roll, pitch and yaw of a ship laboring in heavy weather. This is the compass' final test.

From the final assembly line, the gyro-compass passed into a test room which included swings essentially no different from a lawn or a porch swing, where it rocked as placidly as a summer boarder while inspectors checked and adjusted it at frequent intervals, noting its symptoms on a fever chart attached to the swing. From simple swinging, it graduated to Scorsby machines which counterfeit the roll, pitch and yaw of a ship laboring in heavy weather, counterfeit it so successfully that inspectors surrounded by a bobbing ballet of these machines were known to grow sea-sick from following the gyrations with their eyes.

A compass which continued to register true north after twenty hours of this torture was ready for sea. Sperry specifications allowed an error of .5 degrees plus or minus in the swing test; Dodge held this to .3 degrees. On the Scorsby test, where the Navy allowed a deviation of .6 degrees, Dodge tested to .3 degrees.

Just off the swing, this compass is being adjusted before it moves into the torture-room where the Scorsby machines await it.

One faulty compass which defied diagnosis for many days was found at last to have a fleck of paint on one bearing. That was all, but on a bearing trued to one-ten thousandth of an inch it was enough to disable the entire assembly. These bearings were inspected and guarded in an air-conditioned room like so many incubator babies.

The 5,500th compass did not leave the Dodge plant until early March by when the gyro shop machinery had been dismantled and the working force scattered on other war work. It was waiting for a special name plate which celebrates "Dodge dependability."

As a grateful gesture to the Chrysler Corporation, the Navy has assigned this final compass to a 14,000-ton ship not yet completed at the Philadelphia Navy Yard. This vessel is to become the flagship of the combined chiefs of staff of the amphibious command of one of our joint Army-Navy groups in the Pacific.

The making of gyro-compasses was a semi-secret handicraft in 1942 when the Navy turned to the Chrysler Corporation. That means hand skills, guarded trade secrets, small quantities and slow output, with a necessarily high cost. Small quantities do not permit the high tooling costs of engineered production which produce an automatic accuracy and

Inspectors sometimes become sea-sick in watching the weaving of the compasses on the Scorsby machines.

high output. Different jobs are asked of one machine and one operator, with time-wasting shifting of fixtures. There is no absolute uniformity and therefore no certain interchangeability of parts, for the finest craftsman can not make two identical things; it takes a machine to do this. Hence hours of filing and tailoring are necessary in assembly for exact fit. There was a time when precision could not be had any other way, when mass production was limited to coarser things.

Chrysler has changed this. The Corporation made

One giant Scorsby machine tests gyro-compasses under the extreme conditions likely to be encountered on such ships as destroyer escorts, mine sweepers and convoy patrols.

this intricate and delicate instrument to an accuracy beyond that of handcraft, in any quantity and at any speed the Navy asked for, and at great savings. It did this by applying its technic of engineered production just as it has done with all its war jobs.

Production broke the product down into its simplest components. Tool designers contrived machines and fixtures which left nothing to the judgment and initiative of the operator, transferring the accuracy from the man to the machine. Master Mechanics and Planning laid out the machinery for the smooth, never interrupted flow of parts to sub-assembly, sub-assemblies to final assembly. Each part being micrometrically identical with another of its kind, final assembly was not interrupted. Chrysler purchasing agents bought the materials and pur-

The final package as it left the shipping room—eleven boxes to each unit.

Public exhibition of a gyro-compass undergoing the Scorsby test in the Chrysler building, New York City.

chased parts to best advantage. Chrysler inspectors checked the quality of these materials. Chrysler supervision, watching all, prevented waste. The high first cost of the tooling was recovered many times by the reduction in man hours.

From all this, the saving of nearly $20,000,000 of your tax monies followed almost as automatically as the precision of any gyro-compass part.

Navigating officer consulting a master compass below decks. These compasses require oiling once a week, minor servicing once a month.

51